Usborne Workbooks
Dividing

This book belongs to

....

There are answers on page 27, and notes
for grown-ups at the back of the book.

Here are some of the animals you'll meet in this book.

You can use a pen or pencil to help the animals with their calculations.

Usborne Workbooks
Dividing

Illustrated by Elisa Paganelli

Written by Holly Bathie
Designed by Keith Newell

Kat

Pin

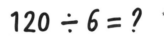

$$120 \div 6 = ?$$

Hop

I've got 120 eggs to pack in boxes of 6. How many boxes is that?

I already know that $12 \div 6 = 2$.

Zeb

120 is ten times bigger than 12, so the answer is ten times bigger.

There are extra pages for your working out at the back of the book.

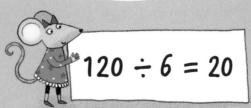

$$120 \div 6 = 20$$

Edited by Kristie Pickersgill
Series Editor: Felicity Brooks

Fact families

Here are 2 rows of 9 apples. 9 x 2 = 18.

Here are 9 columns of 2 apples. 2 x 9 = 18.

Pin

Bruce

Bruce's apples

These 18 apples could be divided into 2 sets of 9. 18 ÷ 2 = 9.

These 18 apples could be divided into 9 sets of 2. 18 ÷ 9 = 2.

Kat

Ping

Multiplication can be done in any order, so you can always write two different multiplying facts using the same numbers, e.g. 9 x 2 = 18 and 2 x 9 = 18.

Dividing is the opposite ('inverse') action to multiplying. So for the two multiplying facts you can make two dividing facts: 18 ÷ 2 = 9 and 18 ÷ 9 = 2.

> 9 x 2 = 18   and   2 x 9 = 18
> 18 ÷ 2 = 9   and   18 ÷ 9 = 2
>
> This set of four related multiplying and dividing facts is called a 'fact family'. You can use fact families to help you with dividing calculations.

The mice want to write another fact family for the number 18. Use the multiplication facts they have written below, to complete the matching dividing ones.

$$3 \times 6 = 18 \qquad 6 \times 3 = 18$$

$$18 \div \boxed{} = \boxed{} \qquad 18 \div \boxed{} = \boxed{}$$

Use your times tables knowledge to complete a fact family for the number 15.

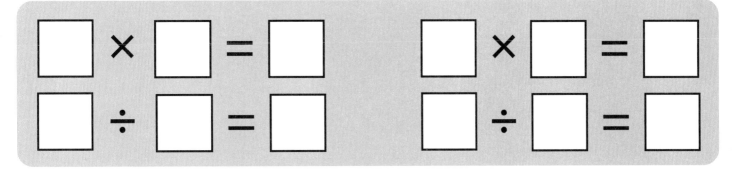

Use your times tables knowledge to complete a fact family for the number 14.

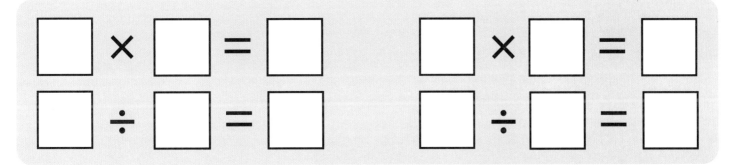

Use your times tables knowledge to complete a fact family for the number 12.

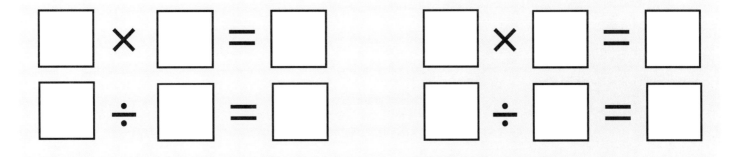

You can practise writing more fact families on page 28.

Dividing using multiplying facts

Ping and Bruce are busy on their market stall.

Ping

We've got 60 plums and I want to put 10 in each bag.

How many bags do we need?

Bruce

PERFECT PLUMS

$$60 \div 10 = \boxed{} \text{ bags}$$

This is Bruce's dividing calculation. He could use related multiplying facts to help him find the answer.

How many times does 10 go into 60?

10, 20, 30, 40, 50, 60... That's six times. 6 x 10 = 60.

Using fact families, I know that the opposite of 6 x 10 = 60 is 60 ÷ 10 = 6.

So to divide 60 plums into bags of 10, we will need 6 bags.

Now complete the dividing calculation above.

Help the other animals at the market by completing their dividing calculations. Think of multiplying facts you know that could help you work out the answer.

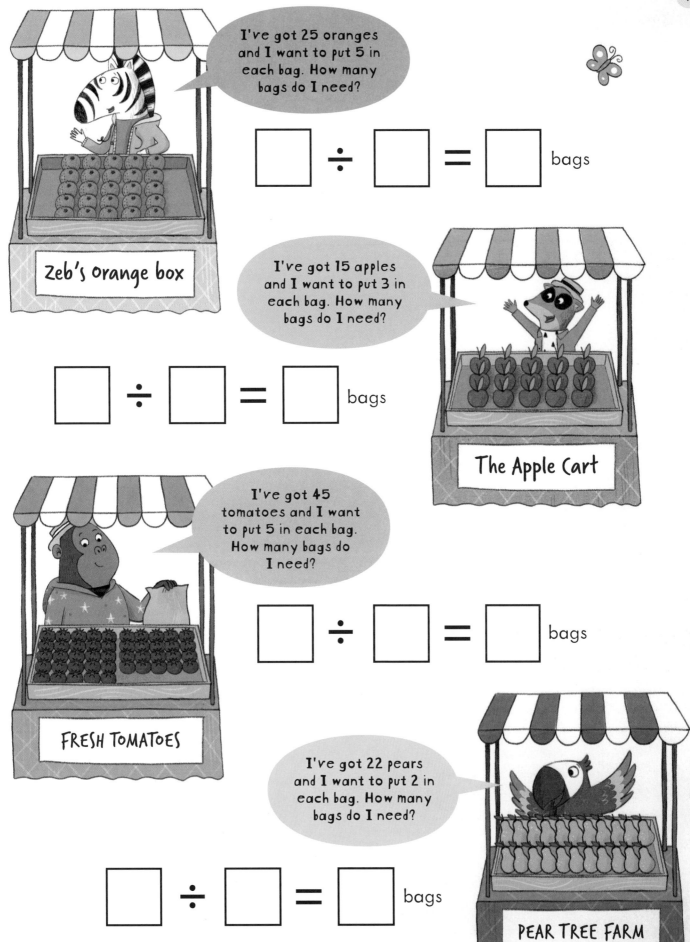

More dividing using multiplying

Ping

This reel of silk ribbon is 75 centimetres long. How much ribbon would you like?

I need ribbons 15 centimetres long for my project. How many could I cut from one reel?

Kat

This is Kat's dividing calculation:

$$75 \div 15 = \boxed{} \text{ ribbons}$$

 How many 15s are in 75? Or, how many times does 15 go into 75?

The mice can use multiplying facts for 15 to help her work out the answer.

Double 15 is 30. So Kat could get at least 2 ribbons out of a reel.

Another 15 is 45. So Kat could get at least 3 ribbons out of a reel.

Another 15 is 60, so Kat could get at least 4 ribbons out of a reel.

We're close, but we haven't reached 75 yet...

$15 \times 2 = 30$

$15 \times 3 = 45$

$15 \times 4 = 60$

$15 \times 5 = 75$

60 add another 15 would be... 75!

15 goes into 75 5 times.

Now complete Kat's dividing calculation above to show how many 15 cm ribbons she could get from one 75 cm reel.

Use multiplying facts to help Ping's other customers below with their calculations. You could use the pages at the back of the book for your working out.

Wolfy

Velvet ribbon
60 cm
per reel

I need velvet ribbons 20 centimetres long. How many velvet ribbons could I cut from one reel?

⬚ ÷ ⬚ = ⬚ velvet ribbons

Bruce

Lace trim
44 cm
per reel

I need lace trim 11 centimetres long. How many pieces could I get from one reel?

⬚ ÷ ⬚ = ⬚ pieces of lace trim

Cotton tape
90 cm
per reel

Hop

I need cotton tape 15 centimetres long. How many pieces could I cut from one reel?

⬚ ÷ ⬚ = ⬚ pieces of tape

Zeb

Elastic
50 cm
per reel

I need elastic 25 centimetres long. How many pieces could I get from one reel?

⬚ ÷ ⬚ = ⬚ pieces of elastic

Fact families with bigger numbers

This is the fact family for 7, 2 and 14. Could we use it to write a fact family with bigger numbers?

Yes, we could write one for 70, 2 and 140.

$$7 \times 2 = 14 \qquad 2 \times 7 = 14$$
$$14 \div 2 = 7 \qquad 14 \div 7 = 2$$

$7 \times 2 = 14$. 70 is ten times bigger than 7. So the answer to 70×2 must be ten times bigger; that's 140.

$14 \div 2 = 7$. 140 is ten times bigger than 14. So the answer to $140 \div 2$ must be ten times bigger; that's 70.

Use this information to complete the fact family below for 70, 2 and 140.

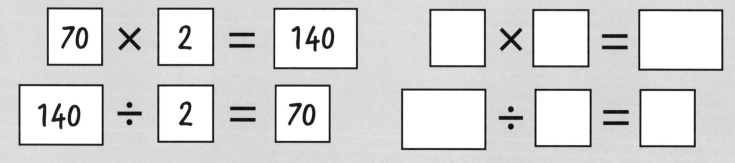

$$70 \times 2 = 140 \qquad \boxed{} \times \boxed{} = \boxed{}$$
$$140 \div 2 = 70 \qquad \boxed{} \div \boxed{} = \boxed{}$$

Now fill in the fact family for 20, 7 and 140.

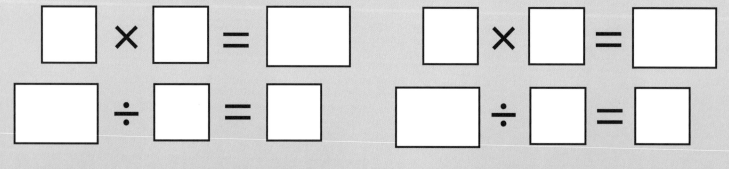

$$\boxed{} \times \boxed{} = \boxed{} \qquad \boxed{} \times \boxed{} = \boxed{}$$
$$\boxed{} \div \boxed{} = \boxed{} \qquad \boxed{} \div \boxed{} = \boxed{}$$

$$150 \div 3 = \boxed{}\ \text{ml}$$

Complete Hop's calculation above, then use your knowledge of times tables and fact families to help these other animals in their baking class.

$$\boxed{} \div \boxed{} = \boxed{}\ \text{g}$$

$$\boxed{} \div \boxed{} = \boxed{}\ \text{g}$$

$$\boxed{} \div \boxed{} = \boxed{}\ \text{ml}$$

Dividing by 4 and 8

320 litres

We're making equal amounts of four milkshake flavours today: vanilla, chocolate, raspberry and banana.

Milk required for today's milkshake flavours, in litres (l)	
Vanilla	l
Chocolate	l
Raspberry	l
Banana	l

Pin

What's 320 litres divided by 4? I know that 32 ÷ 4 = 8...

Use Pin's information, and your knowledge of fact families, to write the amounts of milk needed for each flavour in the table above.

Milk required for today's milkshake flavours, in litres (l)	
	l
	l
	l
	l
	l
	l
	l
	l

Oh, actually we need to make eight flavours today!

Which eight flavours would you make? Write them in the empty table. Then, use your knowledge of fact families for 32 to divide the amount of milk in the tank equally into eight.

Scaling down by 3 and 9

Zeb

This hat stand is 270 centimetres tall, perfect for me!

Hop's Hat Shop

That hat looks fabulous on you, Zeb.

Hmm, Ping I think you will need a hat stand 3 times shorter than Zeb's.

Pat

I want a hat stand too!

Hop

Ping

How tall would my hat stand be?

To make a hat stand that Ping could reach, Hop needs to divide the height of Zeb's hat stand (270 cm) by 3.

270 is ten times bigger than 27. You could write a fact family for 27 first, then use it to help work out the answer to Hop's calculation below.

$$270 \div \boxed{} = \boxed{} \text{ cm}$$

Use the blank pages at the back of the book for your working out.

Hop thinks Pat will need a stand 9 times shorter than Zeb's. Complete the calculation to show how tall Pat's stand needs to be.

$$270 \div \boxed{} = \boxed{} \text{ cm}$$

Dividing using partitioning

To help you solve trickier division calculations, you could use a method called 'partitioning'.

BRUCE'S TIMBER YARD

I have one piece of the wood you want, Gloria. It's 78 centimetres long.

I need 6 pieces of wood, of equal length. If we cut this up, how long would each piece be?

Here is Gloria's calculation:

$$78 \div 6 = \boxed{} \text{ cm}$$

The mice are going to use partitioning to split Gloria's calculation into two easier ones.

Hmm, I've partitioned 78 into tens and units, but I don't think these are easier calculations!

I know that 60 divides by 6, so let's partition 78 into 60 and 18.

That's better, now we can just add the answers together.

$$70 \div 6 = ?$$
$$8 \div 6 = ?$$

We need to partition 78 into two numbers that are easy to divide by 6.

$$60 \div 6 = \boxed{}$$
$$18 \div 6 = \boxed{}$$

Complete these two new calculations for the mice.

$$10 + 3 = 13$$

Now complete Gloria's calculation above.

Use partitioning and your knowledge of fact families to help Bruce's other customers with their calculations.

You could use the partitioning guide on page 29 to help you.

72 cm

I need 4 wooden steps of equal length. If I cut this up, how long would each of my steps be?

☐ ÷ ☐ = ☐ cm

42 cm

I need 3 wooden rods of equal length. If I cut this up, how long would each of my rods be?

☐ ÷ ☐ = ☐ cm

54 cm

I need 3 planks of wood of equal length. If I cut this up, how long would each of my planks be?

☐ ÷ ☐ = ☐ cm

More partitioning

I've only got 98 centimetres of this ribbon left, Hop.

PING'S HABERDASHERY
SALE!

Hmm, I wanted to make 7 identical ribbons out of it. How long would each ribbon be?

Here is Hop's calculation:

 98 ÷ 7 =  cm

Let's split 98 into two smaller numbers that are easier to divide by 7.

I can use my fact family knowledge to help! I know that 70 divides by 7, because 10 lots of 7 is 70.

Use Hop's clue to partition 98 into two numbers that are easier to divide by 7.

98 ➔ ☐
     ➔ ☐

Copy your numbers from the green boxes above into these calculations, then use your knowledge of fact families to divide each one by 7.

☐ ÷ 7 = ☐
☐ ÷ 7 = ☐

Add your answers together, below, to find out how long each of Hop's ribbons will be.

 + = ☐ cm

Now you can complete Hop's calculation at the top of the page.

Use partitioning and your knowledge of fact families to help Ping's other customers with their calculations. You could use the partitioning guide on page 29 to help you.

I need 3 equal pieces of cotton tape. How long would each piece be, if I cut up this length?

Cotton tape: 57 cm

☐ ÷ ☐ = ☐ cm

I need 6 equal pieces of elastic. How long would each piece be, if I cut up this length?

Elastic: 84 cm

☐ ÷ ☐ = ☐ cm

I need 4 equal pieces of lace trim. How long would each piece be, if I cut up this length?

Lace trim: 76 cm

☐ ÷ ☐ = ☐ cm

I need 6 equal length blue ribbons. How long would each ribbon be, if I cut up this length?

Blue ribbon: 96 cm

☐ ÷ ☐ = ☐ cm

Partitioning 3-digit numbers

Sign up here for
Sports Day!

Lots of animals have signed up to events for Zeb's sports day. First, he needs to make teams for the volleyball tournament.

294 animals have signed up! We need 6 in each team. How many teams is that?

This is Zeb's calculation:

$$294 \div 6 = \boxed{} \text{ teams}$$

Use your 6 times table knowledge to split 294 into two numbers that are easier to divide by 6.

6, 12, 18, 24...
24 divides by 6, so 240 must too. We can split 294 into 240 and 54.

If 24 ÷ 6 = 4,
then 240 ÷ 6 = 40.

And I know 9 x 6 = 54,
so 54 ÷ 6 = 9.

$$\underline{24}0 \div 6 = \underline{4}0$$

$$54 \div 6 = 9$$

$$40 + 9 = \ ?$$

Now add the answers together and complete Zeb's calculation above.

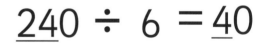

To help you partition 3-digit numbers, use times tables facts of the number you are dividing by.

Use partitioning and your knowledge of fact families to complete Zeb's calculations for the other events. You could use page 29 to help with your partitioning.

112 animals have signed up for the relay races! We need 4 animals in each team. How many teams will that make?

$$112 \div 4 = \boxed{} \text{ teams}$$

315 animals have signed up for the softball tournament! We need 9 animals in each team. How many teams will that make?

$$315 \div 9 = \boxed{} \text{ teams}$$

195 animals have signed up for the basketball tournament! We need 5 animals in each team. How many teams will that make?

$$195 \div 5 = \boxed{} \text{ teams}$$

Short division

When you are dividing numbers that have 3-digits (or more), it can be easier to use a method called 'short division'.

Pin and Kat are going to use short division to help you answer this calculation:

$$936 \div 3 = \boxed{}$$

This is how a short division calculation is laid out.

Each number: 9, 3 and 6, is divided by 3, and the answers are written above the top line.

hundreds   tens   units

9 ÷ 3 is 3. So I write '3' above the line.

3 ÷ 3 is 1. So I write '1' above the line.

6 ÷ 3 is 2. So I write '2' above the line. 312 is the answer!

Complete Kat and Pin's calculation at the top of the page.

Complete the calculations below for Kat and Pin.

$$4 \overline{\smash{)}8\ 4\ 8}$$

$$2 \overline{\smash{)}6\ 8\ 2}$$

$$3 \overline{\smash{)}3\ 6\ 6}$$

Kat and Pin now have a trickier calculation:

$$321 \div 3 = \boxed{}$$

3 ÷ 3 = 1, so I've written '1' above the line. I can't divide 2 by 3; what do I do now?

Write a '0' above the line, then look at the next number along to make a bigger number to divide. Now instead of dividing 2 by 3, you can divide 21 by 3.

$$\begin{array}{c} 1 \\ 3 \overline{\smash{)}\ (3)\ 2\ 1} \end{array}$$

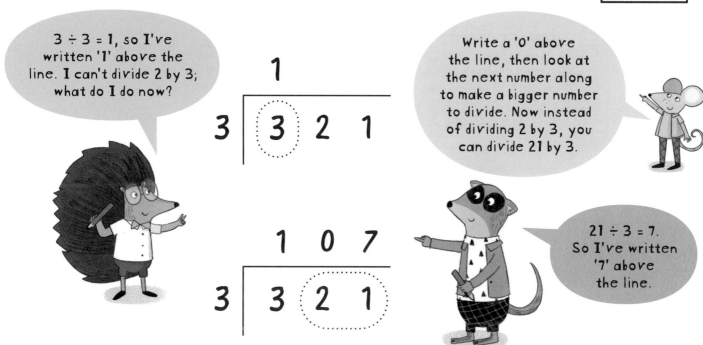

21 ÷ 3 = 7. So I've written '7' above the line.

$$\begin{array}{c} 1\ 0\ 7 \\ 3 \overline{\smash{)}\ 3\ (2\ 1)} \end{array}$$

Write the answer to Kat and Pin's calculation in the box above.

Gloria and Bruce are having trouble in their baking class.
Complete their short division calculations for them.

I need to divide 836 grams of cake mix into 4 tins. How much should be in each tin?

I need to divide 530 grams of cake mix into 5 tins. How much should be in each tin?

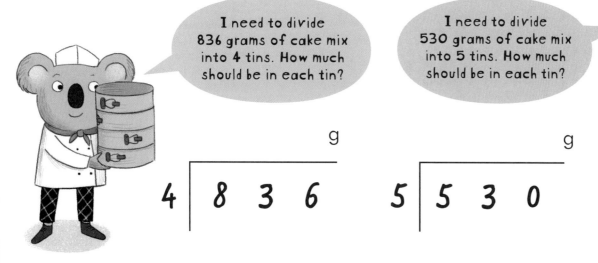

$$4 \overline{\smash{)}8\ 3\ 6} \quad \text{g}$$

$$5 \overline{\smash{)}5\ 3\ 0} \quad \text{g}$$

More short division

Kat and Pin have some more tricky calculations:

$168 \div 4 = \boxed{}$

1 ÷ 4 = ? I can't divide 1 by 4. So I write '0' above the line.

$$\begin{array}{c} 0 \quad 4 \\ \hline 4\,|\,1 \quad 6 \quad 8 \end{array}$$

You still need to use the '1'. If you include the next number along you could make a bigger number to divide by 4. 16 ÷ 4 = 4. So write '4' above the line.

I can divide 8 by 4. 8 ÷ 4 = 2. So I write '2' above the line. The answer is 42.

$$\begin{array}{c} 0 \quad 4 \quad 2 \\ \hline 4\,|\,1 \quad 6 \quad 8 \end{array}$$

$300 \div 5 = \boxed{}$

I can't divide 3 by 5, so I've written '0' above the line. Now I look at 3 and the next number (0) together, which gives 30. 30 ÷ 5 = 6, so I've written '6' above the line.

0 ÷ 5 = 0. So I've written '0' above the line. When you divide 0 by any number, the answer is always 0.

$$\begin{array}{c} 0 \quad 6 \quad 0 \\ \hline 5\,|\,3 \quad 0 \quad 0 \end{array}$$

Write the answer to each of Kat and Pin's calculations in the boxes above.

Fill in and complete the calculations below to help the other bakers.

I need to divide 690 millilitres of oil into 3 tins. How much should be in each tin?

I need to divide 217 millilitres of cream into 7 jars. How much should be in each jar?

ml

3 | 6 9 0

ml

I need to divide 546 millilitres of milk into 6 jugs. How much should be in each jug?

I need to divide 284 grams of cake mixture into 4 tins. How much should be in each tin?

ml

g

I need to divide 400 grams of cake mixture into 8 tins. How much should be in each tin?

I need to divide 963 grams of sugar into 9 bowls. How much should be in each bowl?

g

g

SUGAR

Dividing quiz

Find out how much you can remember about dividing
by doing this quiz. Answers on page 26.

A. Zeb is putting up shelves for his books.
Each shelf can fit 8 books on it.

How many shelves would he need to
put up for 48 books?

 ÷ = shelves

How many shelves would he need to
put up for 72 books?

 ÷ = shelves

How many
shelves will I need
for my books?

Pin is also putting up shelves for her books.
Each of Pin's shelves can fit 10 books on them.

How many shelves would she need for
90 books?

 ÷ = shelves

How many shelves would she need for
110 books?

 ÷ = shelves

B. Finish Ping's fact family for 12, and then use it to help you write a fact family for 3, 40 and 120.

$3 \times 4 = \boxed{}$ $\boxed{} \times \boxed{} = 12$

$12 \div \boxed{} = \boxed{}$ $12 \div \boxed{} = \boxed{}$

$\boxed{} \times \boxed{} = 120$ $\boxed{} \times \boxed{} = 120$

$120 \div \boxed{} = \boxed{}$ $120 \div \boxed{} = \boxed{}$

C. Help Hop and Gloria complete these division calculations. Use partitioning to split each division into two easier calculations.

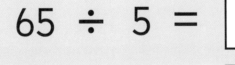

$56 \div 4 = \boxed{}$

$65 \div 5 = \boxed{}$

You could use the partitioning guide on page 29 to help you.

$91 \div 7 = \boxed{}$

$132 \div 6 = \boxed{}$

$168 \div 3 = \boxed{}$

D. Complete these short division calculations for Bruce.

$$3 \overline{)\ 2\ 4\ 6} \qquad 6 \overline{)\ 6\ 5\ 4}$$

$$8 \overline{)\ 2\ 4\ 8} \qquad 4 \overline{)\ 2\ 0\ 4} \qquad 5 \overline{)\ 4\ 0\ 0}$$

Quiz answers

A. $48 \div 8 = 6$
$72 \div 8 = 9$
$90 \div 10 = 9$
$110 \div 10 = 11$

B. $3 \times 4 = 12$ $\qquad 4 \times 3 = 12$
$12 \div 4 = 3$ $\qquad 12 \div 3 = 4$

$3 \times 40 = 120$ $\qquad 40 \times 3 = 120$
$120 \div 40 = 3$ $\qquad 120 \div 3 = 40$

C. $56 \div 4 = 14$
$65 \div 5 = 13$
$91 \div 7 = 13$
$132 \div 6 = 22$
$168 \div 3 = 56$

D. $246 \div 3 = 82$
$654 \div 6 = 109$
$248 \div 8 = 31$
$204 \div 4 = 51$
$400 \div 5 = 80$

Score 1 point for each correct answer and write your score in this box:

22

Answers

Page 5

$18 \div 6 = 3$ $18 \div 3 = 6$

$3 \times 5 = 15$ $5 \times 3 = 15$
$15 \div 5 = 3$ $15 \div 3 = 5$

$7 \times 2 = 14$ $2 \times 7 = 14$
$14 \div 2 = 7$ $14 \div 7 = 2$

$3 \times 4 = 12$ $4 \times 3 = 12$
$12 \div 4 = 3$ $12 \div 3 = 4$
                or
$2 \times 6 = 12$ $6 \times 2 = 12$
$12 \div 6 = 2$ $12 \div 2 = 6$

Pages 6-7

$60 \div 10 = 6$
$25 \div 5 = 5$
$15 \div 3 = 5$
$45 \div 5 = 9$
$22 \div 2 = 11$

Pages 8-9

$75 \div 15 = 5$ $90 \div 15 = 6$
$60 \div 20 = 3$ $50 \div 25 = 2$
$44 \div 11 = 4$

Pages 10-11

$70 \times 2 = 140$ $2 \times 70 = 140$
$140 \div 2 = 70$ $140 \div 70 = 2$

$20 \times 7 = 140$ $7 \times 20 = 140$
$140 \div 7 = 20$ $140 \div 20 = 7$

$150 \div 3 = 50$
$280 \div 4 = 70$
$300 \div 6 = 50$
$560 \div 8 = 70$

Page 12

$320 \div 4 = 80$ litres of each flavour
$320 \div 8 = 40$ litres of each flavour

Page 13

$270 \div 3 = 90$ $270 \div 9 = 30$

Pages 14-15

$78 \div 6 = 13$ $72 \div 4 = 18$
$60 \div 6 = 10$ $42 \div 3 = 14$
$18 \div 6 = 3$ $54 \div 3 = 18$

Pages 16-17

98 could be partitioned into 70 and 28.

$98 \div 7 = 14$ $57 \div 3 = 19$
$70 \div 7 = 10$ $84 \div 6 = 14$
$28 \div 7 = 4$ $76 \div 4 = 19$
$10 + 4 = 14$ $96 \div 6 = 16$

Pages 18-19

$294 \div 6 = 49$
$112 \div 4 = 28$
$315 \div 9 = 35$
$195 \div 5 = 39$

Pages 20-21

$936 \div 3 = 312$
$848 \div 4 = 212$
$682 \div 2 = 341$
$366 \div 3 = 122$
$836 \div 4 = 209$
$530 \div 5 = 106$

Pages 22-23

$168 \div 4 = 42$
$300 \div 5 = 60$
$690 \div 3 = 230$
$217 \div 7 = 31$
$546 \div 6 = 91$
$284 \div 4 = 71$
$400 \div 8 = 50$
$963 \div 9 = 107$

Fact families

You can use this page for writing fact families to help you answer the questions in this book.

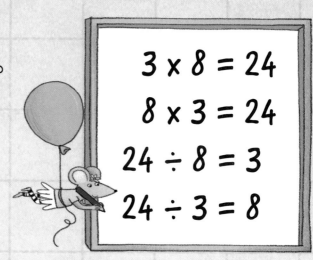

$$3 \times 8 = 24$$
$$8 \times 3 = 24$$
$$24 \div 8 = 3$$
$$24 \div 3 = 8$$

Partitioning guide

The example below shows how to divide a number by splitting it into two easier calculations. You could use the rest of the space on this page for your own partitioning calculations.

Split this number into two new numbers that are easier to divide.

Work out the answers to the two easier divisions.

Add the answers together.

$$84 \div 6 = ?$$

$$60 \div 6 = 10$$

$$24 \div 6 = 4$$

$$14$$

You can use these pages for your working out.

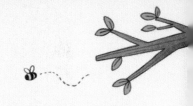

Notes for grown-ups

Fact families (pages 4-5)

Numbers can be multiplied together in any order to give the same answer, so if children know 2 x 5 = 10, then they also know 5 x 2 = 10. The opposite of multiplying by 5 is dividing by 5, so if 2 x 5 = 10, then 10 ÷ 5 = 2. The opposite of multiplying by 2 is dividing by 2, so if 5 x 2 = 10, then 10 ÷ 2 = 5. This set of four related calculations is known as a fact family.

Dividing using multiplying facts (pages 6-7)

These pages encourage children to think of multiplying calculations that could help them to solve their division calculations. Multiplying is the inverse (opposite) of dividing so, for example, if the calculation is 20 ÷ 5, children could count up in 5s to see that 4 lots of 5 is 20, and that means 20 divided by 5 is 4.

More dividing using multiplying (pages 8-9)

Here, children continue to answer dividing questions by counting up in steps (multiplying up) towards a target number. The number of steps it takes to reach their number is the answer to the dividing calculation.

Fact families with bigger numbers (pages 10-11)

Children can use the multiplying facts they already know (from their times tables knowledge) to work out fact families that are ten times bigger. For example, if they know that 15 ÷ 3 = 5, then 150 ÷ 3 must equal 50, because 150 is ten times bigger than 15, so the answer will be ten times bigger than 5.

Dividing by 4 and 8. Scaling down by 3 and 9 (pages 12-13)

These pages give children the opportunity to use fact families to solve dividing problems that involve measurements.

Dividing using partitioning and More partitioning (pages 14-17)

Partitioning a number means splitting it up into two smaller numbers. The number 24 could be split into 20 and 4 (2 tens and 4 units), but it could also be split into 10 and 14. Children can experiment with partitioning numbers in different ways, to find a pair of numbers that make their calculation easier. For instance, they may find the calculation 64 ÷ 4 tricky, but if they split 64 into 40 and 24, they can then answer the easier calculations 40 ÷ 4 and 24 ÷ 4, and add their answers together.

Partitioning 3-digit numbers (pages 18-19)

3-digit numbers can also be split into smaller numbers to make dividing calculations easier. For example, 315 ÷ 5 could be split into 300 ÷ 5 and 15 ÷ 5, which children can answer using their knowledge of the 3 times table.

Short division (pages 20-21)

Short division is an efficient way to divide larger numbers. It is sometimes called 'the bus stop method'.

More short division (pages 22-23)

These pages show children how to tackle some trickier short division questions, such as those involving zeros.